W9-CDF-024

MY SUPER SPOOKY STICKER BOOK

Have fun completing the activities
in this spook-tastic book!

*

Where there is a missing sticker,
you will see an empty shape.
Search the sticker pages
to find the missing sticker.

Then go to the back of the book
to press out and create some
amazing masks!

make
believe
ideas

Slime attack

Color the slime machine.

Sticker the
slimy things.

Splat!

Splat!

Use stickers to finish the pattern.

2

Spooky speed

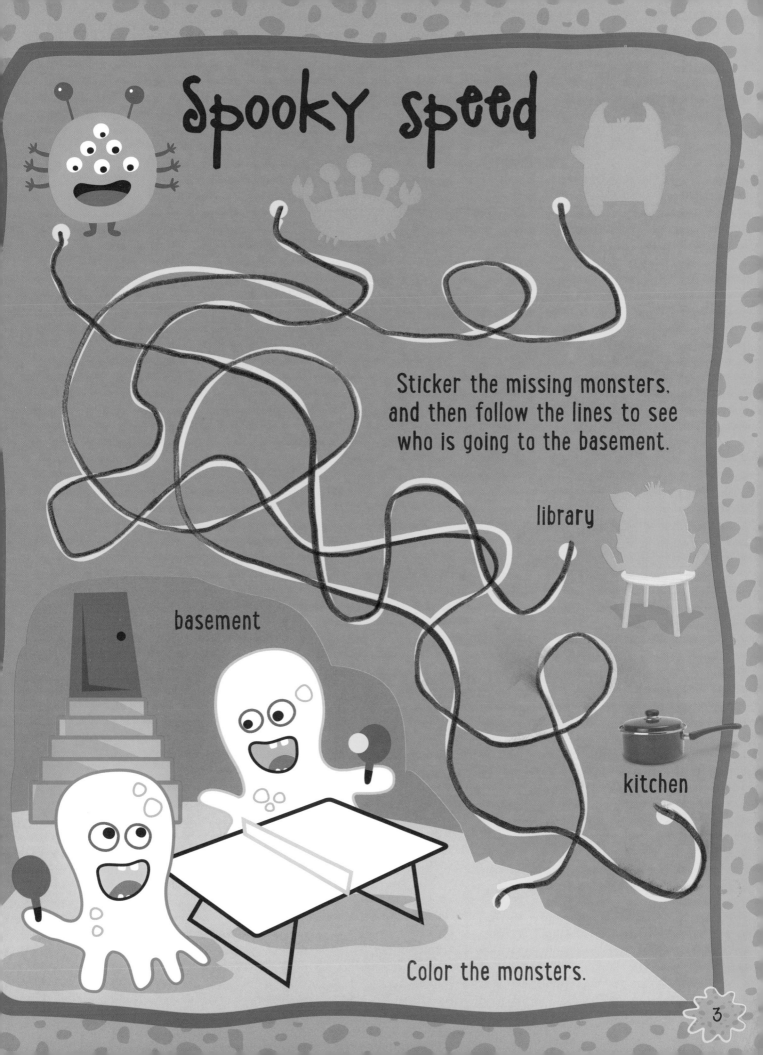

Sticker the missing monsters, and then follow the lines to see who is going to the basement.

library

basement

kitchen

Color the monsters.

Monster cake

Use stickers and color to finish the monster cake.

Boo to you

Color the monster pulling a silly face!

Noisy neighbors

Add color and stickers to finish the scene.

Circle a blue monster.

7

Gem mine

Find the missing stickers, and then help the monster find the gem cave.

Color the gem.

Start

Finish

Warning: Diamond monsters!

8

Mini monsters

Connect the dots and add stickers to see what's in the magnifying glass.

Doodle more fingerprint monsters.

Help, I can't see!

Sticker the monster's eyes, and then draw a mini monster in the magnifying glass.

Monster mayhem

Color the monster. Use the colored dots as a guide.

Scary pairs

FIND the monster who is COPYING me!

Sticker the missing monsters, and then circle two that are exactly the same.

Copy the blue monster.
Trace the dots to get started.

smelly swamp

Add color and stickers to reveal
what critters live in the swamp.

Draw a swamp
monster in the cave.

Circle the yellow monsters.

spooky sweets

Fill the shelves of the candy shop.

Color the
lollipops.

Use color and stickers to finish the display.

fudge

Use the grids to help you draw the missing halves of the candy.

Amazing masks

1 Press out the mask shape, eye holes, and the small holes at either side.

2 Finish the mask using pencils, crayons, and stickers.

3 Ask an adult to thread some elastic or ribbon through the small holes and tie it around your head.

16